Why You're So Hot

1

Your

____

is so hot.

2

It’s so hot how good you are at

____.

3

If you were a spice, you'd be

____________________________________.

4

You are the hottest

____

in the world.

5

It makes me so hot when you

____.

6

Even when you're

____

you're still so hot to me.

7

It would have been wild
to know you when

____.

You look so hot in

____.

9

Remember how crazy
it was the time

______________________________?

10

It's so freakin' hot when you

____

like

____.

11

We'd make a super-hot

team.

12

I dig your taste in

______________________________.

13

It is so hot how you

____.

14

You deserve the Smokin' Hot

____

Award.

15

Your

____

is so hot it should be
studied by science.

16

You're so good at giving

______________________________.

17

If you were an instrument, you'd be

__________________________________.

18

You have the sexiest

____

ever.

19

Your hotness makes me want to

____.

20

It's so hot how you're
usually right about

_______________________________________.

21

I wish I knew your secret for

____.

22

It would be so hot to see you

____.

23

If you wanted to, you could easily

____.

24

People seem to be impressed by your mind-blowing

____.

25

The way you make

____

is so hot.

26

I secretly think it's sexy when you

____.

27

Everyone should be as

____

as you.

28

It's so hot to

____

with you.

29

should play you in the movie of your life.

30

It would be so hot if we

____

someday.

31

I still can't get over how you

____.

32

If we could bottle your

____

and sell it, we'd make a fortune.

33

It's ridiculously hot when you

______________________________________.

34

It's so hot how you
have such strong

______________________________________.

35

If you were a rock star, you'd be

____.

36

It’s so hot how you

____

every day.

37

Your

____

totally turns me on.

38

It's sexy how you want to

____.

39

I never get bored of your

____.

40

It would be so hot to go

____

with you.

41

Watching you

____

is so hot.

42

You make me want to be a better

____.

43

The room temperature rises
when you wear

____.

44

I always want to hear what you're going to say about

______________________________.

45

It's so hot how you believe in

____.

46

If you were a type of candy,
you'd be

______________________________.

47

Nobody else's

____

is as hot as yours.

48

I am so

____

that

________________________________.

49

I am crazy-obsessed
with your

____.

50

Even when you're old, your

____

will always be hot.

You're so hot.

Created and published by Knock Knock
Distributed by Who's There Inc.
Venice, CA 90291
knockknockstuff.com

ISBN: 978-160106672-5 **UPC:** 825703-50070-7

1 2 3 4 5 6 7 8 9 10